BTEC First
Health
and Social Care

STUDY GUIDE

A PEARSON COMPANY

BTEC First Study Guide:
Health and Social Care

Published by:
Edexcel Limited
One90 High Holborn
London WC1V 7BH
www.edexcel.org.uk

Distributed by:
Pearson Education Limited
Edinburgh Gate
Harlow
Essex CM20 2JE

First published 2007
Fifth impression 2009

ISBN 978-1-84690-173-7

Project managed, designed and typeset by Bookcraft Ltd, Stroud, Gloucestershire
Printed by Ashford Colour Press Ltd, Gosport

Cover image © Photofusion Picture Library/Alamy

The Publisher's policy is to use paper manufactured from sustainable forests.

All reasonable efforts have been made to trace and contact original copyright owners.

Contents

Preface

Following a BTEC programme is an exciting way to study. It gives you the opportunity to develop the knowledge, skills and understanding that you will need in the world of work.

BTECs are very different from GCSEs; a BTEC puts *you* in charge of your own learning. This guide has been written specially for you, to help you get started and succeed on your BTEC First course.

The **introduction**, Your BTEC First, tells you about your new course. This will be your companion through the BTEC First, as it:

- tells you how your BTEC will differ from GCSE;

- suggests how you can plan your time;

- explains ways to make the most of visits, guest speakers and work experience;

- advises you about resources and how to find information;

- gives you advice on making presentations and doing assignments.

The **activities** give you tasks to do on your own, in small groups or as a class. You will have the opportunity to put into practice the theory you learn. The activities will help you prepare for assessment by practising your skills and showing you how much you know. These activities are *not* intended for assessment.

The sample **marked assignments** (also sometimes called marked assessments) show you what other students have done to gain a Pass, Merit or Distinction. By seeing what past students have done, you should be able to improve your own grade.

Your BTEC First will cover either three or six units, depending on whether you are doing a Certificate or a Diploma. In this guide the activities cover sections from two units: Unit 1 'Communication and Individual Rights within the Health and Social Care Sectors' and Unit 2 'Individual Needs within the Health and Social Care Sectors'. These units underpin your study of health and social care.

Because the guide covers only two units, it is important that you do all the other work your tutor sets you. Your tutor will ask you to research information in textbooks, in the library and on the internet. You may also have your own textbook for the course: use it! You should have the chance to visit local organisations or welcome guest speakers to your institution. This is a great way to find out more about your chosen vocational area – the type of jobs that are available and what the work is really like.

This guide is a taster, an introduction to your BTEC First. Use it as such, and make the most of the rich learning environment that your tutors will provide for you. Your BTEC First will give you an excellent base for further study, a broad understanding of health and social care and the knowledge you need to succeed in the world of work.

Your BTEC First

Starting a new course is often both exciting and scary. It's normally exciting to do something new, and this includes learning different subjects that appeal to you. BTEC First courses are work-related, so you will be focusing on the work area that interests you. It can be nerve-wracking, though, if you are worried that there may be some topics that you will not understand, if you are unsure how you will be assessed, or if the prospect of some aspects of the course – such as finding out information on your own, or giving a presentation – makes your blood run cold!

It may help to know that these are worries common to many new BTEC First students. Yet every year thousands of them thoroughly enjoy their courses and successfully achieve the award.

Some do this the easy way, while others find it harder.

The easy way involves two things:

- knowing about the course and what you have to do

- positive thinking

Knowledge of the course means that you focus your time and energy on the things that matter. Positive thinking means that you aren't defeated before you start. Your ability to do well is affected by what goes on in your mind. A positive attitude helps you to meet new challenges more easily.

This guide has been written to give you all the information you need to get the most out of your course, to help you to develop positive thinking skills, and, of course, to help you successfully achieve your award. Keep it nearby throughout your course and re-read the relevant parts whenever you need to.

DO THINK	DON'T THINK
I'm quite capable of doing well on this course. First I need to check what I know about it and what I don't – and to fill in the gaps.	*If I struggle a bit or don't like something then so what? I can always drop out if I can't cope.*

Knowing about your course

If a friend or relative asked about your course, what would you say? Would you just shrug or give a vague comment? Or could you give a short, accurate description? If you can do this it usually means that you have a better understanding of what your course is all about – which means you are likely to be better prepared and better organised. You are also more likely to make links between your course and the world around you. This means you can be alert to information that relates to the subject you are studying.

→   Your family, friends, or other people you know may talk about topics that you are covering in class.

→   There may be programmes on television which relate to your studies.

→   Items in the news may be relevant.

→   You may work in a part-time job. Even if your part-time work is in a different area, there will still be useful links. For example, for most BTEC First courses you need to know how to relate to other people at work, how to assist your customers or clients and how to communicate properly. These are skills you need in most part-time jobs.

If you have only a hazy idea about your course then it is sensible to re-read any information you have been given by your school or college and to check further details on the Edexcel website at www.edexcel.org.uk. At the very least, you should know:

- the type of BTEC award you are aiming for and how many units you will be taking:

  ◊   BTEC First Diploma – normally taken as a full-time course, with six units

  ◊   BTEC First Certificate – may be taken as a full-time or part-time course, with three units

- the titles of your core units and what they cover

- the number of specialist units you must take and the options available to you

Core units are compulsory for all students at all centres, and you can find details of them on the Edexcel website. The range of specialist units you can choose will depend upon which award you are taking and where you are studying. Many centres design their courses to meet the needs of the students in their area, in which case you won't have complete freedom to choose your own options. If you do have a choice, find out the content of each of the specialist units available, then think carefully about the ones you would most like to study. Then talk through your ideas with your tutor before you make a final decision.

DO THINK	DON'T THINK
The more I know about my course, the more I can link the different parts together and see how they relate to other areas of my life. This will give me a better understanding of the subjects I am studying.	*It's unlikely that any course will have much relevance to my life or my interests, no matter what anyone says.*

Knowing the difference: BTEC First versus GCSE

BTEC First awards are different from GCSEs in several ways. In addition to the differences in content, the way the topics are taught and the tutors' expectations of their students are also often different. Knowing about these gives you a better idea of what to expect – and how you should respond.

→ BTEC First awards are work-related. All the topics you learn relate to the skills and knowledge you will need in the workplace.

→ They are practical. You will learn how to apply your knowledge, both on your own and as a member of a team, to develop your skills and abilities.

→ Most full-time BTEC First Diploma courses in colleges are completed in one year. If you are taking a BTEC First Certificate course alongside your GCSEs, then you will probably be doing this over two years.

→ There are no exams. So you won't be expected to revise and learn lots of facts, or to write answers to questions in a hot exam room next June. Instead, you will complete assignments set by your tutors, based on learning outcomes set by Edexcel. You can read more about assignments on page 19, but for now you can think of them as being similar to coursework. They will be given to you through the year, and each will have a deadline. See page 19 for advice on coping with assignments, and page 9 for advice on managing your time effectively.

→ On a BTEC First course you will achieve Pass, Merit and Distinctions in your assignments. You will then be awarded an overall Pass, Merit or Distinction for the whole course.

→ BTEC First students are encouraged to take responsibility for their own learning. Your tutors won't expect to have to stand over you all the time to check what you are doing. This helps you to develop the skills to be mature and independent at work. You will be expected to be keen and interested enough to work hard without being continually monitored. You will also be expected to become more self-reliant and better organised as the course progresses. Some students thrive in this situation. They love having more freedom, and are keen to show that they can handle it, especially when they know that they can still ask for help or support when they need it. Other students – thankfully, a minority – aren't mature enough to cope in this situation, so it goes to their head and they run wild.

→ If you've just left school and are going to study for your BTEC First in a college, then you will find many other differences. No bells or uniforms! Maybe fewer timetabled hours; probably longer lesson periods. You will mix with a wider range of people, of different ages and nationalities. You are starting a whole new phase of your life, when you will meet new people and have new experiences. However strange it may seem at the beginning, new students normally settle down quickly. Even if they have been disappointed with some of their grades at GCSE, they are relieved that they can put this disappointment behind them and have a fresh start. If this applies to you, then it's up to you to make the most of it.

DO THINK	DON'T THINK
On my BTEC First course I can find out more about the area of work that interests me. I will enjoy proving that I can work just as well with less direct supervision, and know I can get help and support when I need it.	*Doing a BTEC First will be great because the tutors won't be breathing down my neck all the time and won't care if I mess around on the course.*

Knowing how to use your time

How well organised are you? Do you always plan in advance, find what you've put away, and remember what you've promised to do without being reminded? Or do you live for the moment – and never know what you will be doing more than six hours in advance? Would you forget who you were, some days, unless someone reminded you?

School teachers cope with young students like this by giving homework on set nights, setting close deadlines, and regularly reminding everyone when work is due. They don't (or daren't!) ask students to do something over the next couple of months and then just leave them to it.

Although your BTEC First tutor will give you reminders, he or she will also be preparing you for higher-level courses and for having a responsible job – when you will be expected to cope with a range of tasks and deadlines with few, if any, reminders. On your BTEC First course some work will need to be completed quickly and done for the next session. But other tasks may take some time to do – such as finding out information on a topic, or preparing a presentation. You may be set tasks like this several weeks in advance of the deadline, and it can be easy to put them off, or to forget them altogether – with the result that you may not do the task at all, or end up doing a sloppy job at the last minute because you haven't had time to do it properly.

This problem gets worse over time. At the start of a new course there always seems to be a lot of time and not much pressure: the major deadlines may seem far in the future, and you may find it easy to cope day by day.

This situation is unlikely to last. Some tasks may take you longer than you had thought. Several tutors may want work completed at the same time. And deadlines have a nasty habit of speeding up as they approach. If you have lots of personal commitments too, then you may struggle to cope, and get very stressed or be tempted to give up.

The best way to cope is to learn to manage your own time, rather than letting it manage you. The following tips may help.

→   Expect to have work to do at home, both during the week and at weekends, and plan time for this around your other commitments. It's unrealistic to think that you can complete the course without doing much at home.

→   Schedule fixed working times into your week, taking your other commitments into account. For example, if you always play five-a-side football on Monday evening, keep Tuesday evening free for catching up with work. Similarly, if you work every Saturday, keep some time free on Sunday for work you have to complete over the weekend.

→   Get into the habit of working at certain times, and tell other people in your life what you are doing. If you've no work to do on one of these days, then that's a bonus. It's always easier to find something to do when you unexpectedly have free time than to find time for a task you didn't expect.

→ Write down exactly what you have to do in a diary or notebook the moment you are told about it, so that you don't waste time doing the wrong thing – or ringing lots of people to find out if they know what it is you're supposed to be doing.

→ Normally you should do tasks in order of urgency – even if this means you can't start with the one you like the best. But if, for example, you need to send off for information and wait for it to arrive, you can use the time to work on less urgent tasks.

→ Don't forget to include in your schedule tasks that have to be done over a period of time. It's easy to forget these if you have lots of shorter deadlines to meet. Decide how long the whole task is likely to take you, break the total time up into manageable chunks, and allocate enough time to complete it by the deadline date.

→ Always allow more time than you think you will need, never less.

→ Be disciplined! Anyone who wants to get on in life has to learn that there are times when you have to work, even if you don't want to. Try rewarding yourself with a treat afterwards.

→ If you are struggling to motivate yourself, set yourself a shorter time limit and really focus on what you are doing to get the most out of the session. You may be so engrossed when the time is up that you want to carry on.

→ Speak to your tutor promptly if you have a clash of commitments or a personal problem that is causing you serious difficulties – or if you have truly forgotten an important deadline (then vow not to do so again)!

→ If few of these comments apply to you because you are well organised, hard-working and regularly burn the midnight oil trying to get everything right, then don't forget to build leisure time and relaxation into your schedule. And talk to your tutor if you find that you are getting stressed out because you are trying too hard to be perfect.

DO THINK	**DON'T THINK**
I am quite capable of planning and scheduling the work I have to do, and being self-disciplined about doing it. I don't need a tutor to do this for me.	*I can only work when I'm in the mood and it's up to my tutors to remind me what to do and when.*

Knowing about resources

Resources for your course include the handouts you are given by your tutor, the equipment and facilities at your school or college (such as the library and resource centre), and information you can obtain on the internet from websites that relate to your studies. Resources that are essential for your course – such as a computer and access to the internet – will always be provided. The same applies to specialist resources required for a particular subject. Other resources – such as paper, file folders and a pen – you will be expected to provide yourself.

→ Some popular (or expensive) resources may be shared, and may need to be reserved in advance. These may include popular textbooks in the library, and laptop computers for home use. If it's important to reserve this resource for a certain time, don't leave it till the last minute.

→ You can only benefit from a resource if you know how to use it properly. This applies, for example, to finding information in the library, or using PowerPoint to prepare a presentation. Always ask for help if you need it.

→ You cannot expect to work well if you are forever borrowing what you need. Check out the stationery and equipment you need to buy yourself, and do so before the course starts. Many stationers have discounts on stationery near the start of term.

→ Look after your resources, to avoid last-minute panics or crises. For example, file handouts promptly and in the right place, follow the guidelines for using your IT system, and replace items that are lost or have ceased to work.

DO THINK	DON'T THINK
I have all the resources I need for my course, and I know how to use them or how to find out.	*I can find out what's available if and when I need it, and I can always cadge stuff from someone else.*

Knowing how to get the most from work experience

On some BTEC First courses – such as Children's Care, Learning and Development – all students must undertake a related work placement. On others, work placements are recommended but not essential, or may be required only for some specialist units. So whether or not you spend time on work experience will depend upon several factors, including the course you are taking, the units you are studying, and the opportunities in your own area. You will need to check with your tutor to find out whether you will be going on a work placement as part of your course.

If you need evidence from a work placement for a particular unit, then your tutor will give you a log book or work diary, and will help you to prepare for the experience. You should also do your best to help yourself.

Your placement

→   Check you have all the information about the placement you need, such as the address, start time, and name of your placement supervisor.

→   Know the route from home and how long it will take you to get there.

→   Know what is suitable to wear, and what is not – and make sure all aspects of your appearance are appropriate to your job role.

→   Know any rules, regulations or guidelines that you must follow.

→   Check you know what to do if you have a problem during the placement, such as being too ill to go to work.

→   Talk to your tutor if you have any special personal worries or concerns.

→ Understand why you are going on the placement and how it relates to your course.

→ Know the units to which your evidence will apply.

→ Check the assessment criteria for the units and list the information and evidence you will need to obtain.

<table>
<tr><th>DO THINK</th><th>DON'T THINK</th></tr>
<tr><td>Work experience gives me the opportunity to find out more about possible future workplaces, and link my course to reality.</td><td>Work experience just means I'll be given all the boring jobs to do.</td></tr>
</table>

Knowing how to get the most from special events

BTEC First courses usually include several practical activities and special events. These make the work more interesting and varied, and give you the opportunity to find out information and develop your skills and knowledge in new situations. They may include visits to external venues, visits from specialist speakers, and team events.

Some students enjoy the chance to do something different, while others can't see the point. It will depend on whether or not you are prepared to take an active involvement in what is happening. You will normally obtain the most benefit if you make a few preparations beforehand.

→ Listen carefully when any visit outside school or college, or any arrangement for someone to visit you, is being described. Check you understand exactly why this has been organised and how it relates to your course.

→ Find out what you are expected to do, and any rules or guidelines you must follow, including any specific requirements related to your clothes or appearance.

→ Write down all the key details, such as the date, time, location, and names of those involved. Always allow ample time so that you arrive five minutes early for any special event, and are never late.

→ Your behaviour should be impeccable whenever you are on a visit or listening to a visiting speaker.

→ Check the information you will be expected to prepare or obtain. Often this will relate to a particular assignment, or help you understand a particular topic in more detail.

→ For an external visit, you may be expected to write an account of what you see or do, or to use what you learn to answer questions in an assignment. Remember to take a notebook and pen with you, so that you can make notes easily.

→ For an external speaker, you may be expected to prepare a list of questions as well as to make notes during the talk. Someone will also need to say 'thank you' afterwards on behalf of the group. If your class wants to tape the talk, it's polite to ask the speaker for permission first.

→ For a team event, you may be involved in planning and helping to allocate different team roles. You will be expected to participate positively in any discussions, to talk for some (but not all) of the time, and perhaps to volunteer for some jobs yourself.

→ Write up any notes you make during the event neatly as soon as possible afterwards – while you can still understand what you wrote!

DO THINK	DON'T THINK
I will get more out of external visits, visiting speakers and team events if I prepare in advance, and this will also help me to get good grades.	*Trips out and other events are just a good excuse to have a break and take it easy for bit.*

Knowing how to find out information

Many students who are asked to find out information find it difficult to do so effectively. If they are online, they often print out too much, or can't find what they want. Similarly, too many students drift aimlessly around a library rather than purposefully search for what they need.

Finding out information is a skill that you need to learn. You need to know where to look, how to recognise appropriate information, and when to stop looking in order to meet your deadline, as well as what to do with the information when you've found it.

The first thing to realise is that you will never be asked to find out information for no reason. Before you start, you need to know what you are looking for, why it is needed, where you can find it, and the deadline.

This means you target your search properly and start looking in the right place.

Researching in the library

→   Find out the order in which books are stored. This is normally explained to all students during their induction.

→   Know the other resources and facilities that are available in your library besides books – for example, CD-ROMs and journals.

→   Take enough change with you so that you can photocopy articles that you can't remove. Remember to write down the source of any article you photocopy.

→   If you need specific books or articles, and aren't sure where they will be, try to visit during a quiet time, when the librarian can give you help if you need it.

→   If you find two or three books which include the information you need, that's normally enough. Too many can be confusing.

→   Check quickly if a book contains the information you need by looking in the index for the key words and then checking you can understand the text. If you can't, then forget it and choose another. A book is only helpful to you if you can follow it.

Researching online

→   Use a good search engine to find relevant websites. Scroll down the first few pages of the search results and read the descriptions to see which sites seem to be the best.

→   Remember to read all parts of the screen to check what's available on a website, as menus may be at the foot of the page as well as at the top or on either side. Many large sites have a search facility or a site map which you can access if you are stuck.

→   Don't get distracted by irrelevant information. If your searches regularly lead nowhere, ask your IT resource staff for help.

→   Don't print out everything you read. Even if printouts are free, too much information is just confusing.

→   Bookmark sites you use regularly and find helpful.

Researching by asking other people

This doesn't mean asking someone else to do the work for you! It means finding out about a topic by asking an expert.

→ Think about the people you know who might be able to help you because they have knowledge or experience that would be useful.

→ Prepare in advance by thinking about the best questions to ask.

→ Then contact the person and (unless you know the person well) introduce yourself.

→ Explain politely and clearly why you need the information.

→ Ask your questions, but don't gabble or ask them too quickly.

→ Write notes, so that you don't forget what you are told. Put the name and title of the person, and the date, at the top of the first page.

→ Ask if you can contact the person again, in case there is anything you need to check. Write down their phone number or email address.

→ Remember to say 'thank you'.

Using your information

→ Keep all your information on a topic neatly in a labelled folder or file. If you think you might want to reuse the folder later, put the title on in pencil rather than ink.

→ Refresh your memory of the task by re-reading it before you start to sift the information. Then only select pages that are relevant to the question you have been asked. Put all the other paper away.

→ Remember that you will rarely just be asked to reproduce the information that you have obtained. You will need to make decisions about which parts are the most relevant and how you should use these. For example, if you have visited a sports facility to find out what is available, then you may have to explain which activities are targeted at certain groups of people. You would be expected to disregard information that didn't relate to that task. Or you may be asked to evaluate the facilities, in which case you would have to consider how well the centre met the needs of its users and how it could do better.

→ Never rewrite copied information and pretend they are your own words! This is plagiarism, which is a serious offence with severe penalties. You need to state the source of your material by including the name of the author or the web address – either in the text, or as part of a list at the end. Your tutor will show you how to do this if you are not sure.

→ Write a draft and then ask your tutor to confirm that you are on the right track. You can also check with your tutor if you are unsure whether or not to include certain types of information.

Knowing how to make a presentation

Presentations are a common feature of many BTEC courses. Usually you will be asked to do a presentation as a member of a team. If the team works together and its members support each other then this is far less of an ordeal than it may first seem. The benefits are that you learn many skills, including how to be a team member, how to speak in public, and how to prepare visual aids (often using PowerPoint) – all of which are invaluable for your future career.

Many students get worried about the idea of standing up to speak in front of an audience. This is quite normal, and can even improve your performance if you know how to focus your anxieties productively!

Presentation tasks can be divided into three stages: the initial preparations, the organisation, and the delivery.

Preparation

→   Divide up the work of researching fairly among the team.

→   Bear in mind people's individual strengths and weaknesses and allow for these, so that you all gain from working as a team.

→   Work out how long each person must speak so that you don't exceed your time limit (either individually or as a team).

→   Agree on the type of visual aids that would be best, given your topic. Keeping things simple is often more effective than producing something elaborate that doesn't work properly.

→   Decide on any handouts that are required, prepare these and check them carefully.

→   Check you know when and where the presentation will be held and what you should wear.

→ Think in advance about any questions you may be asked, both individually and as a team.

Organisation

→ Decide who will start and how each person will be introduced. Sometimes the lead person introduces everyone; on other occasions people introduce themselves.

→ Decide the most logical order in which to speak, bearing in mind everyone's contribution and how it fits into the overall presentation.

→ Prepare prompt cards. It's easy to forget some of the things you want to say, so put your main points down in the right order on a prompt card. Never read from this! Instead, write clearly and neatly so that you can just glance down to check on your next point.

→ Check you have sufficient copies of any handouts, and that these are clear and easy to read.

→ Rehearse several times and check your timings.

→ Get your clothes ready the night before.

→ Arrive at the event in plenty of time so that you're not in a rush.

Delivery

→ Take a few deep breaths before you start, to calm your nerves.

→ Make eye contact with your audience, and smile.

→ Keep your head up.

→ Speak a little more slowly than usual.

→ Speak a little more loudly than usual – without shouting.

→ Answer any questions you are asked. If you don't know the answer, be honest – don't guess or waffle.

→ Offer to help a team member who is struggling to answer a question, if you know the answer.

DO THINK	DON'T THINK
If I am well prepared and organised then my presentation will be OK, even if I'm really scared. The audience will always make allowances for some nerves.	*I'm confident about speaking in public so I don't have to bother preparing in advance.*

Knowing the importance of assignments

All BTEC First students are assessed by means of assignments. Each assignment is designed to link to specific learning outcomes. Assignments let you demonstrate that you have the skills and knowledge to get a Pass, Merit or Distinction grade. At the end of your course, your assignment grades together determine the overall grade for your BTEC First Certificate or Diploma.

Each assignment you are given will comprise specific tasks. Many will involve you in obtaining information (see page 14) and then applying your new-found knowledge to produce a written piece of work. Alternatively, you may demonstrate your knowledge by giving a presentation or taking part in an activity.

To get a good grade, you must be able to produce a good response to assignments. To do so, you need to know the golden rules that apply to all assignments, then how to interpret your instructions to get the best grade you can.

The golden rules for assignments

→   Read your instructions carefully. Check that you understand everything, and ask your tutor for help if there is anything that puzzles or worries you.

→   Check that you know whether you have to do all the work on your own, or if you will have to do some as a member of a group. If you work as a team, you will always have to identify which parts are your own contribution.

→   Write down any verbal instructions you are given, including when your tutor is available to discuss your research or any drafts you have prepared.

→ Check you know the date of the final deadline and any penalties for not meeting this.

→ Make sure you know what to do if you have a serious personal problem and need an official extension. An example would be if you were ill and expected to be absent for some time.

→ Remember that copying someone else's work (plagiarism) is always a serious offence – and is easy for experienced tutors to spot. Your school or college will have strict rules which state the consequences of doing this. It is never worth the risk.

→ Schedule enough time for finding out the information and making your initial preparations – from planning a presentation to writing your first draft or preparing an activity.

→ Allow plenty of time between talking to your tutor about your plans, preparations and drafts and the final deadline.

Interpreting your instructions to get the best grade you can

→ Most assignments start with a command word – for example, 'describe', 'explain' or 'evaluate'. These words relate to the level of answer required. A higher level of response is required for a Merit grade than for a Pass, and a higher level still for a Distinction.

→ Students often fall short in an assignment because they do not realise the differences between these words and what they have to do in each case. The tables below show you what is usually required for each grade when you see a particular command word.

→ As you can see from the tables, to obtain a higher grade with a given command word (such as 'describe'), you usually need to give a more complex description or use your information in a different way. You can refer to the example answers to real assignments, and tutor comments, from page 57 onwards.

→ You can check the command words you are likely to see for each unit in the grading grid. It is sensible to read this carefully in advance, so that you know the evidence that you will have to present to obtain a Pass, Merit or Distinction grade.

→ Be prepared to amend, redraft or rethink your work following feedback from your tutor, so that you always produce work that you know is your best effort.

→ Learn how to record your achievement so that you can see your predicted overall grade. Your tutor will show you how to do this, using the Edexcel *Recording your Achievement* form for your subject.

The following tables show what is required to obtain a Pass, Merit and Distinction, for a range of different 'command words'. Generally speaking:

- To obtain a Pass grade, you must be able to show that you understand the key facts relating to a topic.

- To obtain a Merit grade, you must be able to show that, in addition to fulfilling the requirements for a Pass grade, you can also use your knowledge in a certain way.

- To obtain a Distinction grade, you must be able to show that, in addition to fulfilling the requirements for a Pass and a Merit grade, you can also apply your knowledge to a situation and give a reasoned opinion.

Obtaining a Pass

Complete...	Complete a form, diagram or drawing.
Demonstrate...	Show that you can do a particular activity.
Describe...	Give a clear, straightforward description which includes all the main points.
Identify...	Give all the basic facts which relate to a certain topic.
List...	Write a list of the main items (not sentences).
Name...	State the proper terms related to a drawing or diagram.
Outline...	Give all the main points, but without going into too much detail.
State...	Point out or list the main features.

Examples:

- *List the main features on your mobile phone.*

- *Describe the best way to greet a customer.*

- *Outline the procedures you follow to keep your computer system secure.*

Obtaining a Merit

Analyse...	Identify the factors that apply, and state how these are linked and how each of them relates to the topic.
Comment on...	Give your own opinions or views.
Compare... **Contrast...**	Identify the main factors relating to two or more items and point out the similarities and differences.
Competently use...	Take full account of information and feedback you have obtained to review or improve an activity.
Demonstrate...	Prove you can carry out a more complex activity.
Describe...	Give a full description including details of all the relevant features.
Explain...	Give logical reasons to support your views.
Justify...	Give reasons for the points you are making so that the reader knows what you are thinking.
Suggest...	Give your own ideas or thoughts.

Examples:

- *Explain why mobile phones are so popular.*

- *Describe the needs of four different types of customers.*

- *Suggest the type of procedures a business would need to introduce to keep its IT system secure.*

Obtaining a Distinction

Analyse...	Identify several relevant factors, show how they are linked, and explain the importance of each.
Compare... **Contrast...**	Identify the main factors in two or more situations, then explain the similarities and differences, and in some cases say which is best and why.
Demonstrate...	Prove that you can carry out a complex activity taking into account information you have obtained or received to adapt your original ideas.

Describe...	Give a comprehensive description which tells a story to the reader and shows that you can apply your knowledge and information correctly.
Evaluate...	Bring together all your information and make a judgement on the importance or success of something.
Explain...	Provide full details and reasons to support the arguments you are making.
Justify...	Give full reasons or evidence to support your opinion.
Recommend...	Weigh up all the evidence to come to a conclusion, with reasons, about what would be best.

Examples:

- *Evaluate the features and performance of your mobile phone.*

- *Analyse the role of customer service in contributing to an organisation's success.*

- *Justify the main features on the website of a large, successful organisation of your choice.*

DO THINK

Assignments give me the opportunity to demonstrate what I've learned. If I work steadily, take note of the feedback I get and ask for advice when I need it, there is no reason why I can't get a good grade.

DON'T THINK

If I mess up a few assignments it isn't the end of the world. All teachers like to criticise stuff, and I only wanted a Pass anyway.

Knowing what to do if you have a problem

If you are lucky, you will sail through your BTEC First with no major problems. Unfortunately, not every student is so lucky. Some may encounter personal difficulties or other issues that can seriously disrupt their work. If this happens to you, it's vitally important that you know what to do.

→ Check that you know who to talk to if you have a problem. Then check who you should see if that person happens to be away at the time.

→ Don't sit on a problem and worry about it. Talk to someone, in confidence, promptly.

→ Most schools and colleges have professional counselling staff you can see if you have a concern that you don't want to tell your tutor. They will never repeat anything you say to them without your permission.

→ If you have a serious complaint, it's a good idea to talk it over with one of your tutors before you do anything else. Schools and colleges have official procedures to cover important issues such as appeals about assignments and formal complaints, but it's usually sensible to try to resolve a problem informally first.

→ If your school or college has a serious complaint about you, it is likely to invoke its formal disciplinary procedures, and you should know what these are. If you have done something wrong or silly, remember that most people will have more respect for you if you are honest about it, admit where you went wrong and apologise promptly. Lying only makes matters worse.

→ Most students underestimate the ability of their tutors to help them in a crisis – and it's always easier to cope with a worry if you've shared it with someone.

DO THINK	DON'T THINK
My tutors are just as keen for me to do well as I am, and will do everything they can to help me if I have a problem.	*No one will believe I have a problem. Tutors just think it's an excuse to get out of working.*

Finally...

This introduction wasn't written just to give you another task to do! It was written to help you to do your best and get the most out of your course.

So don't just put it on one side and forget about it. Go back to it from time to time to remind yourself about how to approach your course. You may also find it helpful to show it to other people at home, so that they will understand more about your course and what you have to do.

Activities

1   Communication

In this section we will focus on grading criteria P1, P2, M1 and D1 from Unit 1 'Communication and Individual Rights within the Health and Social Care Sectors'.

Those who hope to have a career in health and social care need to understand the skills involved in interpersonal communication. In the following activities you will discover how care workers can enable patients and service users to communicate their needs. You will have the opportunity to investigate many types of communication, both verbal and non-verbal, and the factors that influence them. How can you ensure that you are understood? Do you really mean what you say?

Learning outcomes

Investigate ways of promoting effective communication

Examine barriers to effective communication

Content

Forms of communication: one-to-one; groups; formal; informal; verbal; non-verbal; body language; active listening; facial expression; touch or contact; variation between cultures; the use of signs, symbols, pictures and writing; objects of reference; the use of human and technological aids to communication

Communication cycle: ideas occur; message coded; message sent; message received; message decoded; message understood

Factors that affect communication: e.g. sensory deprivation, foreign language, jargon, slang, dialect, use of acronyms, cultural differences, distress, emotional issues, disabilities, environmental factors, misinterpretation of messages, differing humour, inappropriate behaviour, aggression, feelings of isolation

Ways of overcoming communication barriers: e.g. adapting the environment, understanding language needs and preferences, using the individual's preferred spoken language, active listening, body language, eye contact, proximity, allowing sufficient time, repeating the message, getting individuals to repeat the message, confirming information; alternative forms of communication e.g. sign language, lip-reading, use of signs, symbols, pictures and writing, technological aids to communication; human aids e.g. advocates, interpreters, translators and signers

Grading criteria

P1: participate in one 1:1 interaction and one group interaction and identify the communication skills that contributed to their success

You will observe communication taking place, then undertake an activity that will help you see how good your own skills are.

You will be introduced to the 'communication cycle', a key to successful communication.

P2: identify potential barriers to effective communication and suggest examples of how they can be overcome

You will explore your own communication skills and identify problems that may be holding you back. You will also investigate factors that might influence the effectiveness of communication, and find out what might improve – or spoil – communication.

M1: describe the interactions and suggest additional skills or factors that would have improved communication

Following your own interaction, you will describe how well you think you have communicated and say how it might have been better. You will describe the communication skills of others and say what might be done to improve them. You will examine ways in which verbal and non-verbal communication enables a communication cycle to operate between individuals.

D1: explain how communication skills can be used in a health or social care environment to assist effective communication

In the health and social care setting it might be necessary for you to develop new or different skills to help you communicate with service users. You will give reasons for using those specific skills.

Activity 1

A *glossary* is a list of words and their meanings. It is a useful reference for words that are unfamiliar to you.

As you start to study health and social care you will come across many new words and terms. Copy out a table like the one below to help keep track of these. You can list words, define them and give examples of their use. Each time you come across a new word or phrase, add it to your glossary. If you do this on a word processor it will be easy for you to keep the words in alphabetical order.

Some examples have been given to get you started.

Word	Definition	Example
discriminate	1 – discriminate between – to tell apart 2 – discriminate against – to treat unfairly because of prejudice	*1 – How do I discriminate between the identical twins?* *2 – We have been discriminated against because of our eye colour.*
vulnerable	not protected from emotional or physical harm, or easily tempted	*She is vulnerable because she can't speak clearly.*
socio-economic		
acronym		
stereotype		
prejudice		

Activity 2

Task 1

Communication skills take many forms: talking, writing, smiling, and so on.

On your own, list as many ways of communicating as you can think of.

As a class, brainstorm ideas for ways of communicating. Add to your list any ideas you hadn't thought of.

Task 2

You have listed many different types of communication. Some of these might be used frequently: for example, verbal conversation accompanied by facial expression and body language.

Select a television programme: this could be a 'reality TV' programme, a chat show, or a 'soap'.

Make a table like the one below for your chosen programme. (The example is for *Coronation Street*.) Add any more forms of communication that you can think of.

Watch your chosen programme next time it is on. Select two or three characters to follow, and every time one of your characters uses one of the listed types of communication, put a tick in the relevant box.

At the end of the programme, count the number of ticks in each row.

Coronation Street

Type of Communication	Name of character			
	Steve	Sarah	Jason	Total
verbal				
body language				
facial expression				
touch				
writing				
pictures				
signs or symbols				
technology (e.g. phone)				

What do you notice? Are most of the ticks in the 'verbal' row, or are there more non-verbal ticks?

Some studies suggest that only about 7% of human communication is verbal.

Activity 3

We use non-verbal communication most of the time.

The photographs below all show people using body language or facial expression. For each photograph, say whether they are using body language, facial expression, or both.

© I-Stock

Activity 4

Look at these photographs of people interacting in
pairs or groups. What do you think is going on in
each picture?

Give reasons for your responses.

© I-Stock

© I-Stock

© I-Stock

© BBC

© BBC

Activity 5

Task 1

Make a chart similar to the one below. You might like to add any other forms of communication that you can think of.

Decide on an occasion when you will ask another person to observe you in a conversation or discussion group for five or ten minutes. They should put a tick in the appropriate row every time you use one of the listed types or forms of communication. You should not know when you are being observed.

Name:

Date and time:

Place and occasion:

Type or form of communication	Total number of examples
one to one	
group	
formal	
informal	
verbal	
questioning	
nodding in agreement	
shaking head in disagreement	
making eye contact	
smiling	
frowning	
using hands	
touching	
writing	
drawing	
moving closer	
moving apart	
changing language	
repeating what you've said	
asking for a repeat	
interrupting	
being interrupted	
listening	
turning away	
confirming what was said	

Task 2

Examine the completed chart, count how many ticks are in each row and record the totals in the right-hand column. What does the chart tell you about your communication skills? Do you need to change the way you communicate? Note down the areas that you would like to improve. You can make notes in the space below.

Write a paragraph explaining how you might improve your skills to assist effective communication in the following situations:

- working with the elderly
- working with young children
- at a club
- in a large group
- in an interview

Activity 6

When the communication cycle is working well we understand each other and information is clear.

Task 1

Look at the diagram (below) of a communication cycle. At what points might it break down? Give reasons for your answer.

Task 2

Work in pairs.

Copy (or photocopy) the diagram. Identify a possible break in the cycle, say why the cycle might break there, and how the break could be prevented.

For example: 'message not received'. Why did the service user not receive your information? What would you do to make sure that next time the service user will receive your message?

Make a poster to help other care workers with their communication.

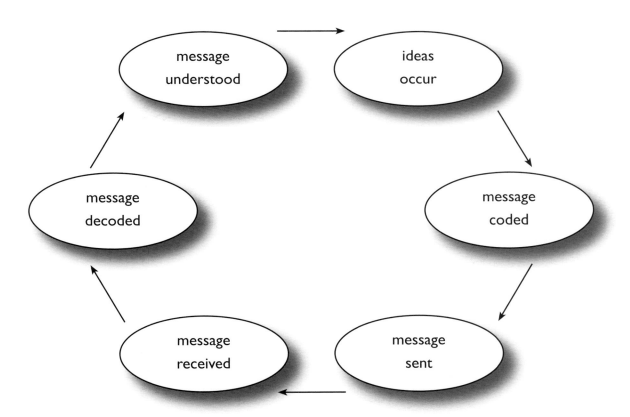

Activity 7

Task 1

Many of the problems that occur in the workplace are a result of poor communication.

As a class, brainstorm a list of possible barriers to communication that you might meet in your work placement. You can make notes in the space below.

Task 2

In a small group, consider the barriers to effective communication that you have listed. Discuss how they might be overcome.

Imagine that you are working in a home for the elderly. Design and construct a poster that shows at least one barrier and its solution. The poster is to go in the staff room to help new staff learn about effective communication.

2   Diversity and equality in society

In this section we will focus on grading criteria P3 and M2 from Unit 1 'Communication and Individual Rights within the Health and Social Care Sectors'.

As a potential worker in health and social care it is important for you to understand issues that might cause individuals to be treated differently, especially in the health and social care environment.

These activities can help you to develop your decision-making skills, through investigating your personal views of the people you work with and the organisations you work in.

Learning outcome

Explore diversity and equality in society

Content

Social factors: e.g. culture, ethnicity, gender, sexuality, age, family structure, social class, geographical location

Political factors: e.g. role of legislation, role of policy, welfare state, the NHS plan

Equality: non-discriminatory practice; discriminatory practice, e.g. discrimination, stereotyping, labelling, prejudice

Grading criteria

P3: identify the factors that contribute to diversity and influence the equality of individuals in society

This means you will need to know what makes us different from each other. Does being treated equally mean being treated the same?

M2: describe the effects of at least six factors on the equality of individuals in society

Activity 1

With a friend, make a list of the differences between you – both physical differences and skills differences.

The list has been started for you, but you will probably be able to think of many more.

	Me	My friend
eye colour		
hair colour		
maths ability		
athletic ability		

You will probably have found many differences, but these will not make any difference to your friendship – in fact, it's the differences between us that make us interesting to each other!

Activity 2

The Care Standards Act 2000 underpins the content of this unit.

Read the following overview of the Act and answer the questions that follow.

The Act has three main areas:

- modernising social services
- regulating private and voluntary healthcare
- regulating early-years education and day care

Under the Act, social care, private healthcare and voluntary care ('care services') will all be regulated by the National Care Standards Commission. 'Care services' will include private hospitals and clinics.

The main purpose of the Act is to reform how the care services in England and Wales are regulated. Care services range from residential care homes and nursing homes, children's homes, domiciliary care agencies, fostering agencies and voluntary adoption agencies through to private and voluntary healthcare services (including private hospitals and clinics and private primary care premises). For the first time, local authorities will have to meet the same standards as independent-sector providers.

For the first time, a register of social care staff will be set up.

The Act imposes a duty on the Secretary of State to maintain a list of individuals who are considered unsuitable to work with vulnerable adults. Care providers will also have to carry out checks and refer to the list before offering employment to potential recruits in a care position working with vulnerable adults.

- What are the three main areas that the Care Standards Act 2000 covers?
- Is there a list of care workers at the moment?
- How will employers know if potential employees are suitable to work with vulnerable adults?
- Will private hospitals be exempt from the new regulations?
- Do local authority care homes have to be of the same standard as private care homes?

Activity 3

What can affect the way we are treated? Do you think you have ever been treated unfairly?

Make a table like the one below. In the left-hand column, list at least six characteristics that could affect the way people are treated. In the right-hand column describe how each of these characteristics might lead to unfair treatment.

Characteristic	Possible unfair treatment

Activity 4

Try to complete the crossword below. You might like to return to the puzzle at intervals throughout the course rather than try to complete it in one go.

You might come across unfamiliar words – don't forget to add them to your glossary.

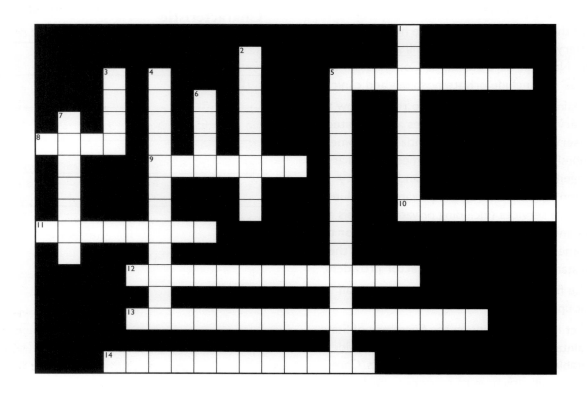

Across

5. Variety, difference

8. 'Inequality runs throughout society': true or false?

9. Carers must ... the rights of all clients.

10. Individuals have the right to be respected and treated ....

11. Most stereotypes are ....

12. The Act in which the main principles of communication and individual rights are set out

13. Rights come with ....

14. Putting people into groups and labelling them

Down

1. A strongly held attitude towards individuals or groups, often negative

2. Equality

3. Does being treated equally mean being treated the ...?

4. It is against the law to ... against a person because of their race, gender or disability.

5. This can damage the quality of client care.

6. Governments have introduced ... to prevent discrimination.

7. Many people who are stereotyped often feel ....

Activity 5

Imagine that your cousin is coming to stay for the weekend – you always have a good time together. Plan the activities, including transport and meals. Will you catch the bus or walk? Eat at home, go out for fast food, or get a takeaway? Will you go to watch sport, or participate? Go to a club? Cinema? Skating? Spare no expense!

Having done that, plan the weekend for the following friends:

- a friend who uses a wheelchair
- a friend who is visually impaired
- a friend whose hearing is impaired

Have you had to change your plans or your timetable?

Prepare a brief presentation to the class to tell them how your plans for one of the three friends above will differ from the plans for your cousin's visit. Explain why you are making the changes.

Activity 6

In pairs, choose one of the two case studies below. Discuss your answers to these questions:

- What issues does this situation raise?
- How would you deal with this situation at the time?
- How would you deal with this situation after the event?
- What attitudes are being demonstrated?

On a flipchart or whiteboard, present your results to the rest of the class.

Case study 1

You are working for a care organisation. You visit people in their own homes to get them ready for bed in the evening.

Your supervisor has told you that one of the clients, Colin, a 29-year-old who is wheelchair-bound, must be visited first (about 7 pm) as he takes so long to deal with. Colin feels that his rights as an individual are not being considered, as he likes to stay up much later.

Case study 2

You are a care assistant in a home for the elderly. A resident, Mrs Brown, aged 87, has been complaining for the last two days about toothache. You tell your shift supervisor, who says: 'Oh, they all have to have something to moan about at that age – just make sure her food is mashed up.'

3   The Care Value Base

In this section we will focus on grading criteria P4, P5, M3 and D2 from Unit 1 'Communication and Individual Rights within the Health and Social Care Sectors'.

The Care Value Base comprises the basic principles and values for carers and service users in health settings. In these activities you will examine how it can be used to promote equality and to foster the rights of service users.

Learning outcome

Investigate how the principles of the Care Value Base can be used to promote the rights of individuals and significant others

Content

Care Value Base: importance of the Care Value Base; how the Care Value Base is incorporated into all health and social care work; codes of practice; policies; charters; the expectations of people receiving the service

Individual rights: rights to be respected; treated equally and not discriminated against; treated as an individual; treated in a dignified way; allowed privacy; protected from danger and harm; allowed access to information about themselves; able to communicate using their preferred methods of communication and language; cared for in a way that meets their needs, takes account of their choices and protects them

Worker's responsibilities: provision of active support to enable patients/service users to communicate their needs, views and preferences; use of communication to support diversity and promote equality of opportunity; confidentiality; disclosure; dealing with tensions between rights and responsibilities; importance of accurate recording; storing and retrieving information; filing correctly and securely; electronic storage; Data Protection Act 1998

Grading criteria

P4: describe the rights of patients/service users

What are the rights of patients and service users? How can you, as a care worker, ensure that your service users receive equality of care?

What are your rights as an individual?

P5: identify the principles of the Care Value Base and care workers' responsibilities to patients/service users

What is the Care Value Base? You will have to be able to describe its main points. You must also describe the responsibilities that care workers have for their service users.

You will have the opportunity to investigate these questions by completing exercises that will develop your understanding and knowledge.

You will need to describe what the Care Value Base is, and how aspects of this important set of principles relate to care workers' practice.

M3: use examples to describe how the principles of the Care Value Base and care workers' responsibilities promote patients'/service users' rights.

Can you get hold of information that others (for example, your doctor) hold about you?

Can patients and service users make decisions that their carers disagree with?

To satisfy this criterion you must use examples – probably from your work placement – that describe how the Care Value Base can support the rights of service users. You must also give examples of the responsibilities that care workers have to improve service users' rights.

D2: explain how the principles of the Care Value Base and care workers' responsibilities can be applied to promoting patients'/service users' rights

How can the care worker apply the Care Value Base to ensure that service users, whatever their ability, benefit from their rights?

What are the responsibilities of the care worker regarding service users' confidences?

When, if ever, is the care worker justified in disclosing a service user's confidence?

Activity 1

The Care Value Base (CVB) is a set of five principles and values that were devised in 1992 for all workers in health and social care.

The CVB covers five main areas:

- anti-discriminatory practice
- confidentiality
- individual rights
- personal beliefs and identity
- effective communication

Anti-discriminatory practice

Discrimination is outlawed by:

- the Sex Discrimination Act 1975
- the Race Relations Act 1976
- the Disabled Persons Act 1986 (amended 2005)

Age discrimination became prohibited by the end of 2006. Laws prohibiting discrimination on grounds of religion or belief were introduced in 2005–06.

Confidentiality

Clients have a right to expect that information about them will be kept confidential. There are three main Acts that cover this confidentiality:

- the Data Protection Act 1987
- the Access to Health Records Act 1990

- the Access to Personal Files Act 1987

However, in each Act provision has been made for care workers to breach confidentiality where there is risk to clients or others (your tutor will cover this area in more depth).

Individual rights

Health workers should encourage and enable clients to make decisions about their care and treatment.

Personal beliefs and identity

All users of health and social care have a right to privacy and a right to maintain their own beliefs in relation to self, religion, ethics, culture and sexual preference.

Effective communication

Effective communication can be defined as the exchange of thoughts, messages, or information by speech, signals, writing or behaviour.

Research each of the five main areas of the Care Value Base, using the library, the internet or your textbook. You can make notes in the space below.

Give an example relating to each, linked to your work placement. If you have not been on placement yet, link your example to a television programme or to a situation of your choice.

Activity 2

The grid below contains 15 words or phrases particularly important to the Care Value Base. They may be placed horizontally, vertically, or diagonally.

As you find each word or phrase, find a reference to it in this book, and copy the reference into your workbook.

B	L	G	Q	Q	P	Y	M	S	V	A	R	Z	V	V	L	V	Q	M	R	K	I	R	X	Y
V	P	K	B	X	S	R	E	Y	C	C	O	N	F	I	D	E	N	T	I	A	L	I	T	Y
I	R	F	V	E	R	O	G	R	P	N	U	F	W	M	P	H	A	B	H	J	D	H	S	I
O	E	I	L	V	L	I	C	F	I	V	E	P	R	I	N	C	I	P	L	E	S	Q	L	D
H	J	S	D	Z	R	I	G	I	Y	T	W	H	E	A	L	T	H	R	E	C	O	R	D	S
Q	U	T	A	I	R	R	E	H	A	T	R	E	V	R	X	I	F	K	U	T	L	U	H	J
D	D	E	K	E	V	I	B	F	T	L	H	U	E	D	R	I	F	K	M	V	L	S	L	F
N	I	R	G	V	A	E	C	V	S	S	C	Q	S	K	P	A	F	E	Y	Q	N	A	H	X
W	C	E	M	M	E	O	R	W	N	H	P	L	U	T	T	K	B	L	S	V	A	H	J	I
F	E	O	Y	J	G	Q	Y	S	B	T	B	X	A	L	N	N	C	U	G	T	J	H	Y	F
U	A	T	Z	N	J	O	I	W	I	N	A	I	P	S	D	T	T	I	S	R	Y	A	N	R
K	Y	Y	Z	M	G	V	X	P	L	T	I	J	S	S	S	T	O	E	L	Q	P	L	G	V
D	S	P	W	J	O	B	H	A	E	D	Y	V	L	L	C	G	W	H	V	I	M	Z	E	Y
L	I	E	F	F	E	C	T	I	V	E	C	O	M	M	U	N	I	C	A	T	I	O	N	S
J	D	S	G	G	B	K	P	P	R	E	S	P	O	N	S	I	B	I	L	I	T	I	E	S
Y	M	M	L	E	Q	L	O	L	E	G	A	L	R	E	Q	U	I	R	E	M	E	N	T	S
V	S	E	X	D	I	S	C	R	I	M	I	N	A	T	I	O	N	A	C	T	U	K	F	Z

- FIVE PRINCIPLES
- SEX DISCRIMINATION ACT
- HEALTH RECORDS
- EFFECTIVE COMMUNICATION
- TRUST
- LEGAL REQUIREMENTS
- RIGHTS
- BELIEFS

- STEREOTYPES
- PREJUDICE
- DIVERSITY
- CONFIDENTIALITY
- SOCIAL CLASS
- LIFESTYLES
- RESPONSIBILITIES

Activity 3

Imagine that the organisation where you are undertaking your work placement is setting up a new care home. As you have a good understanding of the Care Value Base you have been asked to devise a 'charter of responsibilities', which will be framed and placed in the entrance hall for visitors, residents and care workers to see. On your own or in pairs, prepare a poster for display. If possible, use IT to create it.

Your charter should:

- describe the rights of the service users, and what they should expect from the workers in this home
- give examples of choices that residents should expect
- explain the responsibilities of the care workers
- consider legal requirements regarding confidentiality of personal records
- recognise diversity

Activity 4

Read the following scenarios. In pairs, discuss what the next steps should be in each case.

Scenario 1

Each service user at your work placement has a separate file relating specifically to them, which is secured in a locked cabinet. One of the residents has demanded to read the notes in his file and has asked if you will get them for him. You know that you must inform the nurse in charge. What do you think the response will be?

Scenario 2

Ruby, one of the elderly residents at the care home where you do your work placement, looks forward to you coming on duty, as you take time to listen to her; she trusts you and has told you all about her life. One day Ruby tells you in confidence that she has had enough of life – she is 87 years old, and has been saving up her sleeping tablets to take in one go. Ruby can no longer walk and needs help with all of her personal needs; her family have not visited her for many months; you feel sorry for her and the sad situation that she is in.

Scenario 3

You overhear the following conversation between a resident and one of your colleagues (Sarah):

Sarah: 'Come on Mr Brown, finish your supper.'

Mr Brown: 'You put sugar in my tea – I don't take sugar.'

Sarah: 'Yes, you do, you always have sugar – the other nurse told me so.'

Mr Brown: 'No, I can't drink it – take it away!'

Sarah: 'Come on, you need more fluids, you're getting confused.'

Mr Brown: 'No, no!'

Sarah: 'All right then, it's time for bed anyway.'

Mr Brown: 'But I want to watch the television in the sitting room – it's only 7:30.'

Sarah: 'Well, we need to get tidied up ready for the night staff – we can't just do what you want, you know.'

In groups, discuss the ways in which the Care Value Base is being ignored. Present your findings to the rest of the class.

Activity 5

On your own, investigate your rights: what rights do you have, and how are they protected? Is there legislation that will support you if your rights are abused? You can make notes in the space below.

Work in groups. Select two or three of the following candidates for 'rights', and for each one try to find out whether it is protected and whether there is legislation to support you if it is not respected. It might be helpful to devise a chart that you can use to present your findings.

'Rights'

- to be respected
- to be treated equally and not be discriminated against
- to be treated as an individual
- to have privacy
- to be protected from danger
- to see any information about oneself
- to communicate freely
- to have freedom of choice
- to be cared for in a way that meets my needs

4   Everyday needs of individuals in society

In this section we will focus on grading criteria P1, P2, P3, M1, M2 and D1 from Unit 2 'Individual Needs within the Health and Social Care Sectors'.

Workers in health and social care must have a good understanding of the everyday needs of individuals, and must appreciate the consequences of these needs not being fully met.

The following activities will enable you to examine and understand the needs of people in society. You will investigate those needs that you have in common, and those that are different from others. You will investigate issues that might affect the health and needs of individuals.

As you work through the activities, don't forget to add new words to your glossary. You might like to compare your glossary with those of your friends: do they have any words that you have not included?

Learning outcomes

Explore the everyday needs of individuals in society

Examine factors that influence the health and needs of individuals

Content

Needs: Maslow's hierarchy

Physical needs: e.g. food, water, shelter, warmth, safety

Social needs: e.g. to belong, acceptance, family, friends, group membership, relationships

Emotional needs: e.g. relationships, love, friendship, affection, esteem

Intellectual needs: e.g. stimulating environment, esteem, achievement e.g. work/career

Physical factors: biological inheritance; environment

Socio-economic factors: social class; employment; housing; income; education; accessibility to services; media; gender; culture; religion

Lifestyle factors: personal hygiene; diet; physical exercise; substance abuse (alcohol, illegal or legal drugs), smoking; stress; sexual practices

Abuse: physical; emotional; sexual

Harm: short-term; medium-term; long-term; self-harm

Action plan: short, medium and long-term goals; objectives/outcomes; realistic e.g. financial factors, time constraints, social factors

Grading criteria

P1: describe the everyday needs of individuals in society

You will research the everyday needs of individuals and compare different people's needs.

P2: identify the potential effects of four factors that can influence the health and subsequent needs of individuals in society

You will investigate influences on health and explore the needs that might result.

P3: produce a realistic action plan to improve the health of a chosen individual

You will produce a plan that will help improve the health of one person.

M1: explain the potential effects of four factors that can influence the health and subsequent needs of individuals in society

You will give reasons why certain factors might change the health and needs of individuals.

M2: describe factors which may influence the ability of the individual to adhere to an action plan

You will investigate the reasons why an individual might not stick to an action plan.

D1: explain the potential physical, social and emotional effects on the individual achieving the targets in the action plan

You will explore the possible results of your action plan.

Activity 1

We all have needs. Some are the same for everyone, but others are individual.

Task 1

With a partner, list the needs that you have in common. Remember, needs are not the same as wants!

Task 2

List your own, individual, everyday needs.

When you have completed your list, choose two examples from the following list, and write down the everyday needs of each of those people.

- a 17-year-old man who is confined to a wheelchair
- a pregnant asylum-seeker who cannot speak much English
- an elderly lady who has had a stroke and lives in a care home
- a teenage diabetic
- a healthy 5-year-old
- a professional footballer
- a homeless person
- a single parent with two children under 5 years of age

Task 3

Compare your three lists.

Write a short article on the differences between them, and explain why the needs are different for each person.

Activity 2

The diagram below represents Maslow's hierarchy of needs.

Copy the diagram onto a large sheet of paper and complete the blank parts.

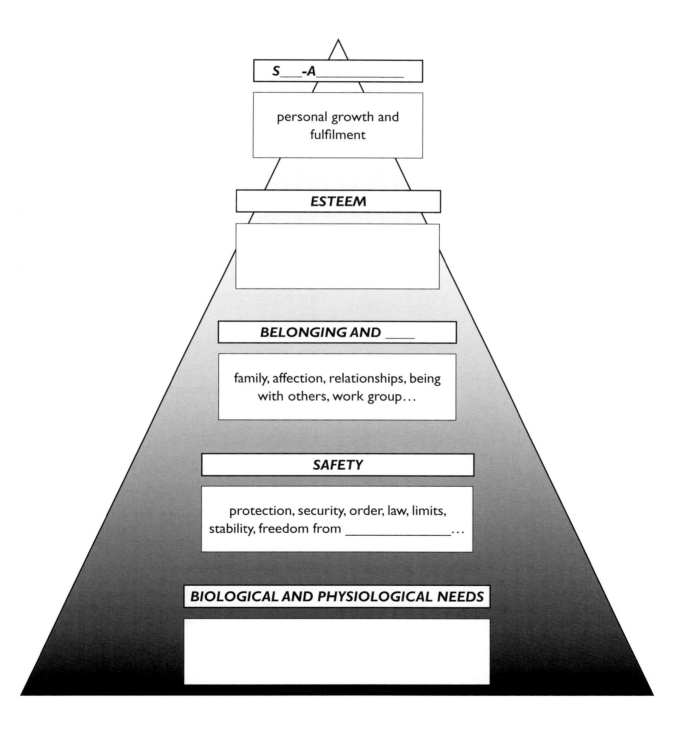

S___-A_____

personal growth and fulfilment

ESTEEM

BELONGING AND ____

family, affection, relationships, being with others, work group…

SAFETY

protection, security, order, law, limits, stability, freedom from _____…

BIOLOGICAL AND PHYSIOLOGICAL NEEDS

Activity 3

The passages below addresses some of the factors that influence the health and needs of individuals. Use these words or phrases to fill in the gaps. Use each word only once.

- seven to nine
- sweaty
- drink
- men
- stopping
- vigorous
- small
- 21 units
- healthy
- fruit and vegetables
- half a pint
- 30
- weight
- smoke
- women
- 14 units
- walk
- 5–10%
- breath
- five

What can I do to help stay healthy?

Don't _____.

If you smoke, _____ smoking is often the single most effective thing that you can do to reduce your risk of future illness. The risk to health starts to fall rapidly as soon as you stop smoking.

Do some regular physical activity.

Anything that gets you mildly out of _____ and a little _____ is fine – for example, jogging, heavy gardening, swimming, or cycling. A brisk _____ each day is what many people do to get their exercise. However, it is thought that the more _____ the activity, the better. To gain most benefit you should do at least _____ minutes of physical activity on most days.

Eat a _____ *diet.*

A healthy diet means eating plenty of _____. Government guidelines suggest eating at least _____ varied portions, and ideally _____ portions, per day.

Try to lose _____ *if you are overweight or obese.*

You don't need to get to a perfect weight. If you are overweight you can greatly improve your health by losing _____ of your weight. This might be between 5 and 10 kg. (10 kg is about one-and-a-half stone.)

Don't _____ *too much alcohol.*

A _____ amount of alcohol is usually fine, but too much can be harmful. According to government guidelines, _____ should drink no more than _____ per week (and no more than 4 units in any one day), while _____ should drink no more than _____ per week (and no more than 3 units in any one day). One unit is about _____ of normal-strength beer, or two-thirds of a small glass of wine, or one small pub measure of spirits.

Activity 4

It is not easy to change your lifestyle, but to improve health, changes have to be for life. This means that any change must be realistic: it must be practical and reasonable.

Design and produce a plan for someone you know. This could be yourself, a friend, or a member of your family. You can just choose one area that will improve health – for example, stopping smoking or starting to exercise – or you might aim for a general, all-round health improvement.

The plan should be written (or word-processed), and could contain a timeline if changes are to take place in stages.

Activity 5

Task 1

Look at the picture of the young man on the right. He is waiting for his favourite meal – shown below – which his mother prepares for him several times each week.

Do you think this is a healthy meal to be eating several times each week?

Write a letter to this young man explaining why you think he should change some of his habits. Use the internet, magazines and books to find pictures of meals that you think might be acceptable alternatives for him, and include these in your letter.

© I-Stock

© I-Stock

Task 2

In a small group (no more than four people), look at the pictures again.

On a flipchart, list the factors that might affect the health of the young man. Also list the effects that the young man might experience when trying to swap his unhealthy habits for a more healthy lifestyle.

Discuss and list the possible effects should the young man not make any changes to his lifestyle.

Task 3

There could be many reasons why the young man in the picture might have difficulty changing his lifestyle.

On your own, write a short paragraph explaining why he might have difficulty sticking to an action plan. Suggest some solutions that might help him address his difficulties.

Here are some of the difficulties he may face. There could be many more:

- He does not like being told what to do.
- Everyone he lives with smokes.
- Everyone he works with smokes.
- He doesn't think he has enough money to eat healthily.
- He doesn't think he has enough money to join a gym.

Activity 6

With a friend, copy the chart below onto a large poster.

In the appropriate columns, list the positive effects of achieving targets for a healthy lifestyle.

Some factors have been included. Add as many more as you can.

Factor	Physical effect	Social effect	Emotional effect
giving up smoking			
trying to achieve a healthy weight			
starting to exercise			
cutting down on alcohol			
giving up drugs			
practising 'safe' sex			

Activity 7

Who do you think could be affected by harm or abuse?

How do you think harm and abuse could affect the health and needs of people?

With a partner, design a leaflet that makes people aware of the effects that harm and abuse could have on their health.

Remember that abuse can affect all age groups, from tiny babies to the very old, and that physical abuse is not the only kind.

Activity 8

Bullying is a serious form of abuse, and can cause all types of harm: physical, emotional, financial, psychological, and so on.

Task 1

Using textbooks and the internet, research:

- who bullies are
- why they bully

Task 2

The people below can all be victims of bullying:

- an elderly person in a care home
- a secretary in an office
- a shop assistant
- a nurse
- a teenager who walks to school each day
- a 15-year-old boy who is bigger than everyone else in his class
- a young teacher who is new to a school
- a 5-year-old who has a different background from the rest of the class

In groups of four, choose one of the examples above and design posters to help that category of victim. How will they know they are being bullied? What can they do about it? The poster should have the following title: 'Those who can, do – those who can't, bully'.

The poster should indicate the form that the bullying is taking: for example, intimidation, demanding, racial abuse, isolation, fault-finding, or violence. It should also indicate steps that can be taken to help the person being bullied.

Task 3

In the same groups, present your posters to the rest of the class.

Explain who is being bullied, and how.

Describe what might happen if the bullying continues.

Describe how the person being bullied can get help.

Activity 9

Read through the list below. This is the new occupational scale that replaces the Registrar General's social class scale.

1   higher managerial and professional occupations

1.1   employers and managers in larger organisations (e.g., company directors, senior company managers, senior civil servants, senior officers in police and armed forces)

1.2   higher professionals (e.g., doctors, lawyers, clergy, teachers, social workers)

2   lower managerial and professional occupations (e.g., nurses and midwives, journalists, actors, musicians, prison officers, lower ranks of police and armed forces)

3   intermediate occupations (e.g., clerks, secretaries, driving instructors, telephone fitters)

4   small employers and own-account workers (e.g., publicans, farmers, taxi drivers, window cleaners, painters and decorators)

5   lower supervisory, craft and related occupations (e.g., printers, plumbers, television engineers, train drivers, butchers)

6   semi-routine occupations (e.g., shop assistants, hairdressers, bus drivers, cooks)

7   routine occupations (e.g., couriers, labourers, waiters, refuse collectors)

8   the long-term unemployed

In pairs, discuss the following questions and write down your answers, giving reasons.

Why should people in group 1 be considered to have a better lifestyle than all the rest?

Why should the people in group 8 have poorer health than those in all the other groups?

Some musicians and sportspeople are amongst the highest-paid people in the country. Do you think they are amongst the healthiest people in the country?

Answers to Activity 2.4 (p 38)

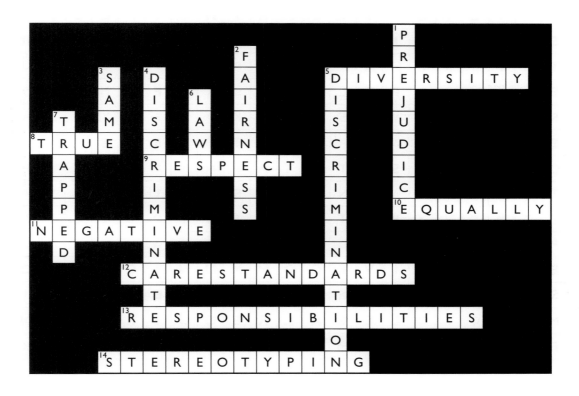

Answers to Activity 3.2 (p 42)

B	L	G	Q	Q	P	Y	M	S	V	A	R	Z	V	V	L	V	Q	M	R	K	I	R	X	Y
V	**P**	K	**B**	X	**S**	R	E	Y	C	**C**	**O**	**N**	**F**	**I**	**D**	**E**	**N**	**T**	**I**	**A**	**L**	**I**	**T**	**Y**
I	**R**	F	V	**E**	**R**	**O**	G	R	P	N	U	F	W	M	P	H	A	B	H	J	D	H	S	I
O	**E**	I	L	V	**L**	**I**	**C**	**F**	**I**	**V**	**E**	**P**	**R**	**I**	**N**	**C**	**I**	**P**	**L**	**E**	**S**	Q	L	D
H	**J**	**S**	D	Z	R	**I**	**G**	**I**	Y	**T**	W	**H**	**E**	**A**	**L**	**T**	**H**	**R**	**E**	**C**	**O**	**R**	**D**	**S**
Q	**U**	**T**	A	**I**	R	R	**E**	**H**	**A**	T	**R**	E	V	R	X	**I**	F	K	U	T	L	U	H	J
D	**D**	**E**	K	E	**V**	I	B	**F**	**T**	**L**	H	**U**	E	D	R	I	**F**	K	M	V	L	S	L	F
N	**I**	**R**	G	V	A	**E**	C	V	**S**	**S**	**C**	Q	**S**	K	P	A	F	**E**	Y	Q	N	A	H	X
W	**C**	**E**	M	M	E	O	**R**	W	N	H	P	**L**	U	**T**	T	K	B	L	**S**	V	A	H	J	I
F	**E**	**O**	Y	J	G	Q	Y	**S**	B	T	B	X	**A**	L	N	N	C	U	G	**T**	J	H	Y	F
U	A	**T**	Z	N	J	O	I	W	**I**	N	A	I	P	**S**	D	T	T	I	S	R	**Y**	A	N	R
K	Y	**Y**	Z	M	G	V	X	P	L	**T**	I	J	S	S	**S**	T	O	E	L	Q	P	**L**	G	V
D	S	**P**	W	J	O	B	H	A	E	D	**Y**	V	L	L	C	G	W	H	V	I	M	Z	**E**	Y
L	I	**E**	**F**	**F**	**E**	**C**	**T**	**I**	**V**	**E**	**C**	**O**	**M**	**M**	**U**	**N**	**I**	**C**	**A**	**T**	**I**	**O**	**N**	**S**
J	D	**S**	G	G	B	K	P	P	**R**	**E**	**S**	**P**	**O**	**N**	**S**	**I**	**B**	**I**	**L**	**I**	**T**	**I**	**E**	**S**
Y	M	M	L	E	Q	L	O	**L**	**E**	**G**	**A**	**L**	**R**	**E**	**Q**	**U**	**I**	**R**	**E**	**M**	**E**	**N**	**T**	**S**
V	**S**	**E**	**X**	**D**	**I**	**S**	**C**	**R**	**I**	**M**	**I**	**N**	**A**	**T**	**I**	**O**	**N**	**A**	**C**	**T**	U	K	F	Z

Answers to Activity 4.2 (p 47)

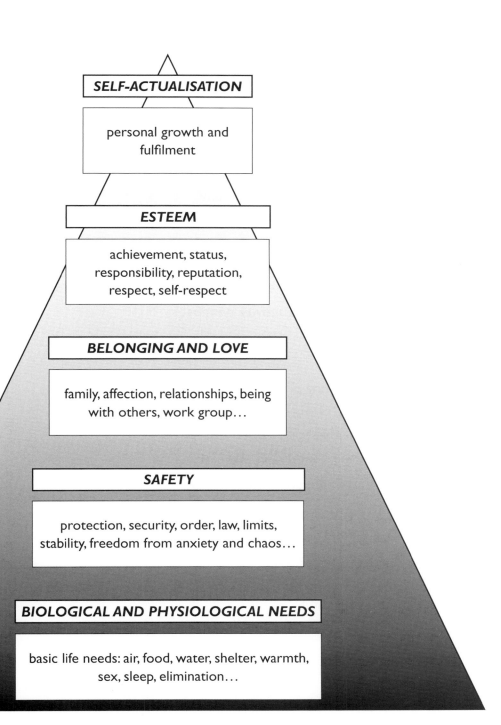

SELF-ACTUALISATION

personal growth and fulfilment

ESTEEM

achievement, status, responsibility, reputation, respect, self-respect

BELONGING AND LOVE

family, affection, relationships, being with others, work group…

SAFETY

protection, security, order, law, limits, stability, freedom from anxiety and chaos…

BIOLOGICAL AND PHYSIOLOGICAL NEEDS

basic life needs: air, food, water, shelter, warmth, sex, sleep, elimination…

Answers to Activity 4.3 (p 48)

What can I do to help stay healthy?

Don't **smoke**.

If you smoke, **stopping** smoking is often the single most effective thing that you can do to reduce your risk of future illness. The risk to health starts to fall rapidly as soon as you stop smoking.

Do some regular physical activity.

Anything that gets you mildly out of **breath** and a little **sweaty** is fine – for example, jogging, heavy gardening, swimming, or cycling. A brisk **walk** each day is what many people do to get their exercise. However, it is thought that the more **vigorous** the activity, the better. To gain most benefit you should do at least **30** minutes of physical activity on most days.

Eat a **healthy** *diet.*

A healthy diet means eating plenty of **fruit and vegetables**. Government guidelines suggest eating at least **five** varied portions, and ideally **seven to nine** portions, per day.

Try to lose **weight** *if you are overweight or obese.*

You don't need to get to a perfect weight. If you are overweight you can greatly improve your health by losing **5–10%** of your weight. This might be between 5 and 10 kg. (10 kg is about one-and-a-half stone.)

Don't **drink** *too much alcohol.*

A **small** amount of alcohol is usually fine, but too much can be harmful. According to government guidelines, **men** should drink no more than **21 units** per week (and no more than 4 units in any one day), while **women** should drink no more than **14 units** per week (and no more than 3 units in any one day). One unit is about **half a pint** of normal-strength beer, or two-thirds of a small glass of wine, or one small pub measure of spirits.

Marked assignments

Exemplar assignment

Unit 2 – Individual Needs within the Health and Social Care Sectors

Assignment 1 – Individual Needs

This assignment will help meet learning outcomes:

- Explore the everyday needs of individuals in society
- Examine factors that influence the health and needs of individuals

Scenario:

Everyone in the world has needs – we all have some needs that are the same e.g. we all need air to breath and food and water to keep us alive, and without sex the human race would die out!

We also have some needs that are different for each person, for example we have different learning needs according to the career or life we want to live, we have diverse emotional and social needs that differ from one society or culture to another.

Although we all have some basic needs that are the same, how we meet those needs might be different for each of us – for example we all need to eat, but we do not all eat the same type of food.

Why do we make the choices that we do? Especially if we are aware that our decision might cause us harm?

In this assignment you will use your knowledge and information that you have gained from reading and research to investigate the everyday needs of individuals in society.

This assignment will enable you to show that you can:

- (P1) describe the everyday needs of individuals in society
- (P2) identify the potential effects of four factors that can influence the health and subsequent needs of individuals in society
- (P3) produce a realistic action plan to improve the health of a chosen individual
- (M1) explain the potential effects of four factors that can influence the health and subsequent needs of individuals in society

- (M2) describe factors which may influence the ability of the individual to adhere to an action plan
- (D1) explain the potential physical, social and emotional effects on the individual achieving the targets in the action plan

Remember that you must list your reference sources at the end of your work in a bibliography. This should include the titles of websites and newspapers or magazines that you have used, the titles and authors of textbooks that you have referred to and information from any other leaflets, booklets or documents that you have quoted.

Task I (PI)

The diagram below depicts a 'hierarchy' of needs (Abraham Maslow's 1954). Lower level needs must be met in order for us to progress to higher levels. For example, if care workers are satisfied with food, water and safe working conditions, they are more likely to concentrate on working well within their teams.

Using the diagram, select and describe the everyday needs of individuals giving examples of how those needs are met. (PI)

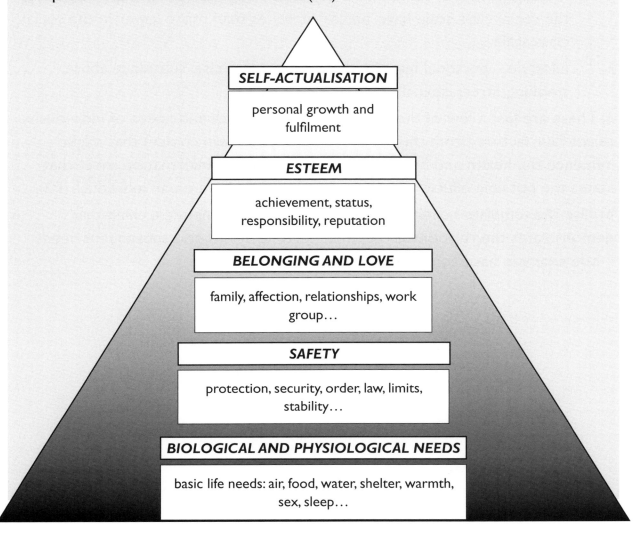

Task 2 (P2, M1)

In Task 1 you identified the everyday needs of individuals. Now, you will investigate influences (factors) on those needs and how they might affect future needs.

Factors that might influence the health and needs of people include:

- Housing – a large house in the country or a small, cramped, damp inner-city flat
- Environment – surroundings, an overcrowded town with a high level of unemployment and a high crime rate or a small town with high employment, low crime rate and good community facilities
- Access and availability – geographical location; those in the centre of town are surrounded by shops, medical facilities, leisure resorts etc those in rural settings are surrounded by farms and woodland
- Genetics – inherited disorders or disabilities e.g. some types of hearing disorder; Down's Syndrome; some heart conditions etc
- Social class – groups of people sharing broadly similar types and levels of resources, with broadly similar styles of living – those who are higher up the social class scale have 'better' lifestyles than those lower in the social class scale
- Lifestyle – personal hygiene, diet, physical exercise, substance abuse, smoking, stress, sexual practices

a) These are just a few of the influences on the health and needs of individuals, select four factors (from the list above or of your own choice) that might influence the health and needs of people. Produce an information sheet that states the possible effects that these factors might have on an individual. (P2)

b) Use the template headings on the next page to complete a chart that demonstrates the relationship between factors, health, and subsequent needs – one example has been given. (M1)

Factor	Influence on health	Subsequent needs
Lifestyle, diet	A poor diet that is nutritionally imbalanced – high in fat, salt, sugar and low in fibre – can contribute to obesity, high blood pressure, heart disease etc and lead to inability to exercise, stress on joints, shortness of breath etc.	Dependence on medication; inability to carry out everyday activities – shopping, dog walking etc, so dependent on carer; need for costly medical care, tests, hospitalisation etc.

Task 3 (P3, M2, D1)

a) Select one individual, this could be someone known to you or an imaginary person. Give a brief biography stating gender, age, lifestyle and any other details that might affect their ability to make choices and decisions. You might find it helpful to devise a short questionnaire that considers the individual's current lifestyle.

Devise an action plan that might help improve the health of your individual. You might find it easier to have short, medium and long term targets for the individual. (P3)

b) Success on achieving targets set in the action plan can be enormous – giving greater benefits than just those intended! Explain the potential physical, social and emotional effects on the individual who achieves their target. (D1)

c) Not everyone finds an action plan easy to stick with! List and describe the factors that might influence the individual to adhere to or to give up their action plan. (M2)

Pass level answer

Faisal Ahmed – Task 1 (P1)

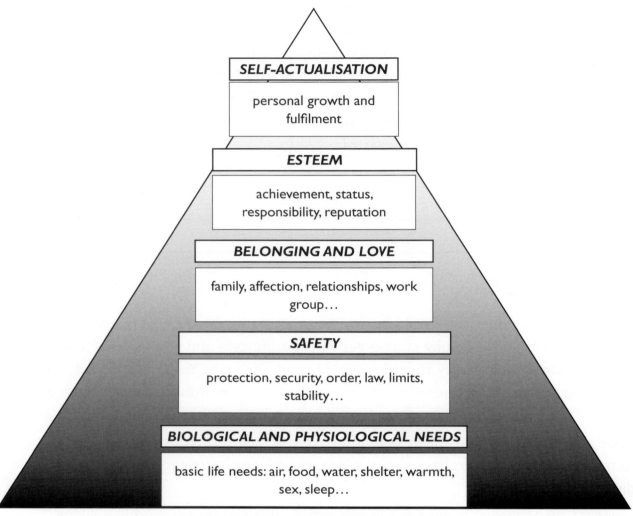

Lower level needs must be met in order for us to progress to higher levels. For example, if care workers are satisfied with food, water and safe working conditions, they are more likely to concentrate on working well within their teams.

Using the diagram, select and describe the everyday needs of individuals giving examples of how those needs are met.

Not all of the subjects identified in Maslow's Hierarchy of Needs are 'everyday' needs, our most basic needs are inborn and without these we cannot survive as individuals – or as a race!

Apart from our everyday, basic needs, we have other requirements that differ from person to person, and are met differently according to our upbringing, culture and social needs.

The everyday needs required by individuals in society that I have identified are:

Need	Example of how met
Air	The air that we breathe is a mixture of gases including nitrogen, oxygen and other gases. The composition of air is crucial to life if the balance of gases is upset we would not survive. The balance of gases is changed when anaesthetic is given, this is in a controlled environment that ensures the patient receives only sufficient for the procedure.
Food	Food is also essential to sustain life. However, not all food is nutritionally necessary, for example, sugar, that many people add to drinks etc, does not contribute to nutrition as it adds only calories – no protein, carbohydrates, vitamins or minerals! A well balanced diet is met through an intake of food that provides sufficient energy to maintain the functions of life.
Drink	The human body is composed of 65% water, and will only survive for eight to ten days without it. The body requires approximately eight to ten cups of water each day to replace that lost in sweat and urine. Water needs are increased if a person suffers from diarrhoea or vomiting or undergoes heavy physical exercise. It is advisable to avoid drinks containing caffeine or alcohol as those are both diuretics that cause an increase in urine output.
Shelter	Shelter at its most basic level gives protection from the elements and danger, and privacy to the individual. Following a disaster, shelter is often lacking and is a resource that can be provided by others in the form of tents or temporary accommodation.

Need	Example of how met
Warmth	Warmth is another basic requirement; the human body will not tolerate extremes of temperature and should be maintained at 37°C. Should the temperature of the body fall below 35°C hypothermia will occur. Extremes of temperature (below 35°C or above 40°C) can lead to death.
Sex	Sex, or reproduction, ensures that the human race survives. Genes are passed on from the parents that carry characteristics of hair and eye colour; there is much debate about the passing on of personality and behaviour in the genes, this is referred to as the Nature/Nurture debate.
Sleep	Sleep is a natural state of rest that should not be confused with unconsciousness. It is thought that sleep is a time for healing and growth, but there are many differing theories regarding the value of sleep. One theory indicates that memory is highly dependent on sleep. Information is initially stored temporarily, and transferred to long-term storage during sleep.
Safety	Safety is defined as the state of being safe. Maslow uses 'safety' as an entire category, that includes protection, security, order, law, limits, stability – not all of these are basic everyday needs for individuals, however, together they are. The individual must remain safe and protected from all types of undesirable behaviour or event whatever the cause, these would include, abuse, accidents, harm etc.

Tutor Feedback

Name: Faisal Ahmed

Task 1 (P1)

Faisal, this is a well written assignment, meeting the assessment criteria for P1.

You have described the everyday needs of individuals in society so meeting the assessment criteria for P1.

In addition you have given examples describing how the basic everyday needs are met, and have discussed your reasons for including those needs and excluding others.

Well done.

Pass/Merit level answer

Bernadette O'Donnell – Task 2 (P2, M1)

a) Select four factors (from the list or of your own choice) that might influence the health and needs of people. Produce an information sheet that states the possible effects that these factors might have on an individual. (P2)

b) Use the template headings below to complete a chart that demonstrates the relationship between (four) factors, health, and subsequent needs – one example has been given. (M1)

a)

Four factors that might influence the health and needs of people include the following:

Lifestyle, smoking.

Individuals choose whether to smoke or to not smoke. Those who choose to smoke do so for many reasons the commonest of which is peer pressure. Other reasons that individuals smoke include – helping to deal with stress and enjoying the taste. Smoking is an addiction, once addicted individuals might choose to buy cigarettes in preference to healthy meals.

Housing.

If you live in a large house in the country you might have better health as you are not surrounded by industry and commerce with all the pollution. You might also be able to get fresher food and milk which is better for your diet.

Employment, employed – on minimum wage.

Someone who is employed might be able to afford a better lifestyle – diet, exercise, private health care etc, but if they are on a minimum wage only they might be worse off than someone who is unemployed. This is because the person who is unemployed might be entitled to free prescriptions and dental care. They might also get benefits that give them more disposable income than the person who is on minimum wage.

Harm, abuse

If someone is being abused, physically, sexually, through neglect or any other form of abuse – their health might be affected both mentally and/or physically. Abuse can lead to poor self-esteem, this in turn can lead to someone not taking care of their health and well-being.

The Effects of Four Factors on Your Life!

	Positive	Negative
Lifestyle – Smoking	Gives a (false) feeling of stress release; makes you one of the crowd.	Raises blood pressure; causes lung disease; harms unborn babies; makes individual and their clothes and homes, smell!
Housing – country	Fresh air, lots of open spaces to walk in. No air pollution, less traffic. Good food available.	A long distance from social life so might become withdrawn.
Employment – minimum wage	Positive psychological effect as feel part of society and making contributions to the home.	Might be worse of as have to pay for medication and health care. Might not be entitled to free school meals etc.
Harm – abuse	No positive effects.	Physical and psychological damage which might be long term and permanent.

b) a chart that demonstrates the relationship between (four) factors, health, and subsequent needs – one example has been given

Factor	Influence on health	Subsequent needs
Lifestyle, diet (example)	A poor diet that is nutritionally imbalanced – high in fat, salt, sugar and low in fibre – can contribute to obesity, high blood pressure, heart disease etc and lead to inability to exercise, stress on joints, shortness of breath etc.	Dependence on medication; inability to carry out everyday activities – shopping, dog walking etc, so dependent on carer; need for costly medical care, tests, hospitalisation etc.
Lifestyle – smoking	The chemicals present in tobacco can damage body tissues and cause many types of disease and disability. E.g. raised blood pressure; male impotence; lung disease; heart disease. Smoking has been linked with lung cancer and damage to unborn babies.	The subsequent needs of the individual will depend on the damage caused by smoking. Hospitalisation and medical care might be required, these would be costly to the country not only monetary terms but also in time lost from work for ill health.

Factor	Influence on health	Subsequent needs
Housing – country	Living in the country might have benefits as the individual will be able to walk in the fresh air. The person who lives in the country might have a poor social life and become withdrawn and suffer from depression.	This individual will need long term counselling and may need psychiatric care.
Employment	The person who is only paid minimum wage might be worse off than the person who is unemployed.	They might have to pay for medication and health care. Might not be entitled to free school meals etc.
Harm – abuse	The person who is being or has been abused is likely to suffer from low self-esteem with all the problems that this has. They might well turn to drug abuse as a way out of their problems.	The individual might not have a nutritionally balanced diet as they do not care about appearance or health. If they are using drugs they might turn to crime or prostitution to pay for the habit. These things in turn have the potential to damage health through STDs, and further psychological damage which will require long term treatment and medical intervention.

Tutor Feedback

Name: Bernadette O'Donnell
Task 2 (P2, M1)

Bernadette, you have selected four factors that can influence the health of individuals; lifestyle; housing; employment; harm; and have discussed the potential effects and subsequent needs of individuals.

Your discussion has made several generalisations that should be considered e.g. living in a large house in the country does not necessarily mean that you will be more healthy than living in a small house in the town! The large house dweller might have inherited an old, ramshackle home that is too costly to repair – also remember that very little of the food produced in this country is sold at the site of production so country dwellers must be able to get to shops and many villages no longer enable affordable shopping for local people.

Living in the town or in a city can also be very lonely, those who are in the country might belong to local organisations and have a better social life than their urban colleagues!

I think you might have found it easier to produce a straightforward factual leaflet rather than attempting to look at positive and negative views, a very difficult task!

By identifying the potential effects of four factors that can influence the health of individuals in society you have achieved P2.

To achieve M1 you need to give more explanation of the effects of the four factors you have chosen, you have only explained the possible effects on health and subsequent needs of three – smoking, housing and abuse.

What influence might employment on minimum wage have on the health and needs of the individual? You need to expand on your answer to b), giving more detail and explanation.

Bernadette O'Donnell – Task 2 (P2, M1)

Resubmission

b) Use the template headings below to complete a chart that demonstrates the relationship between (four) factors, health, and subsequent needs – one example has been given. (M1)

Factor	Influence on health	Subsequent needs
Lifestyle, diet (example)	A poor diet that is nutritionally imbalanced – high in fat, salt, sugar and low in fibre – can contribute to obesity, high blood pressure, heart disease etc and lead to inability to exercise, stress on joints, shortness of breath etc.	Dependence on medication; inability to carry out everyday activities – shopping, dog walking etc, so dependent on carer; need for costly medical care, tests, hospitalisation etc.
Lifestyle – smoking	The chemicals present in tobacco can damage body tissues and cause many types of disease and disability. E.g. raised blood pressure; male impotence; lung disease; heart disease. Smoking has been linked with lung cancer and damage to unborn babies.	The subsequent needs of the individual will depend on the damage caused by smoking. Hospitalisation and medical care might be required, these would be costly to the country not only monetary terms but also in time lost from work for ill health.

Factor	Influence on health	Subsequent needs
Housing – country	Living in the country might have benefits as the individual will be able to walk in the fresh air. The person who lives in the country might have a poor social life and become withdrawn and suffer from depression.	This individual will need long term counselling and may need psychiatric care.
Employment	The person who is only paid minimum wage might be worse off than the person who is unemployed. *If they earn too much to claim benefits they might also have to pay for prescriptions, dental care and eye care. They might not be able to afford to buy enough fruit and vegetables for a healthy diet – they might find it cheaper to fill up on fatty, high calorie food which could lead to obesity, high blood pressure and heart attack.*	*If this person does not get dental care they might develop mouth infections and bad teeth. Also if they do not get regular eye care diseases like glaucoma might be missed until it causes severe damage.* *The needs caused by poor diet would depend on the disease, but might require medication, time in hospital or long term illness and inability to work.*

Factor	Influence on health	Subsequent needs
Harm – abuse	The person who is being or has been abused is likely to suffer from low self-esteem with all the problems that this has. They might well turn to drug abuse as a way out of their problems.	The individual might not have a nutritionally balanced diet as they do not care about appearance or health. If they are using drugs they might turn to crime or prostitution to pay for the habit. These things in turn have the potential to damage health through STDs, and further psychological damage which will require long term treatment and medical intervention.

Tutor Feedback

Name: Bernadette O'Donnell

Task 2 (P2, M1)

Resubmission

Bernadette, you have added much more information and this is certainly the level of work I would expect from a student wishing to gain a Merit. Together with the earlier part of the assignment, I can now confirm that you have achieved P2 and M1.

Pass/Merit/Distinction level answer

Jenny Smith – Task 3 (P3, M2, D1)

a) Select one individual, this could be someone known to you or an imaginary person. Give a brief biography stating gender, age, lifestyle and any other details that might affect their ability to make choices and decisions. You might find it helpful to devise a short questionnaire that considers the individual's current lifestyle.

Devise an action plan that might help improve the health of your individual. You might find it easier to have short, medium and long term targets for the individual. (P3)

b) Success on achieving targets set in the action plan can be enormous – giving greater benefits than just those intended! Explain the potential physical, social and emotional effects on the individual who achieves their target. (D1)

c) Not everyone finds an action plan easy to stick with! List and describe the factors that might influence the individual to adhere to or to give up their action plan. (M2)

a)
A realistic action plan to improve the health of a chosen individual

I have chosen to devise an action plan for Deirdre Barlow from Coronation Street (Wikipedia). Deidre is aged 51, currently married to Ken (she has been married five times, twice to Ken!), and has one daughter, Tracy, and one granddaughter, Amy.

Deidre's household comprises herself, husband Ken, mother Blanche and a little dog. From time to time Tracy and Amy live with them in the small terrace house.

Deirdre is a heavy smoker and has a gravely voice resulting from this. Deidre appears to drink alcohol quite frequently; it is difficult to assess her diet as she does not appear to eat very much. She does not take any exercise.

Deidre seems to have quite a stressful life as her family cause her many problems.

ACTION PLAN FOR DEIDRE BARLOW

1) – to stop smoking

2) – to start exercising

3) – to eat a well balanced diet

4) – to reduce the stress in her life

In order for this to be a realistic action plan with a chance of Deirdre succeeding all targets should not be addressed at once. The time scale for achieving the targets should be practical and reasonable.

The plan should be discussed with Deidre, informing her of the benefits of each of the changes she would be making, she should also be told of the dangers of continuing as she does.

Points 1–3 would greatly reduce the stress in her life, so addressing point 4 will be less arduous.

As Deidre has been smoking for many years she might find this the hardest challenge to meet and will need time to get used to the idea of giving up. This will be the last target to be addressed.

Although Deidre does not look over weight, her diet might be high in salt – which contributes to high blood pressure; and in saturated fats – which increase cholesterol levels and can lead to stroke or heart disease.

Deidre should be given a 'food diary', to complete over a one week period. This would show the areas that need changing and will allow time to think about the health benefits of changing her diet.

PLAN

Week	1	2	3
Diet	Complete food diary. Do not eat meals in front of the television. Concentrate and enjoy what you are eating. Cut down on number of packets of crisps and savoury snacks each day.	Introduce fish into meals at least twice weekly (high in omega 3 and low in saturated fat). Replace butter/ marge with low fat spread. Take a packed lunch to work instead of going to the pub or the chip shop. Remove salt pot from meal table.	Replace sugar in drinks with sweeteners – or cut out completely. Ensure eating at least 5 portions of fruit or vegetables each day. Reduce number of times have red meat each week (high in saturated fat).
Exercise	Get off bus one stop earlier. Find a 'buddy' to start exercising or dance classes with.	Use stairs instead of lifts or escalators in shops. Investigate local dance clubs or fitness centres.	Try to carry out twenty minutes of exercise at least three times each week
Smoking	Find out about NHS Smoking Helpline	Find out about 'Smokefree Together' programme. See GP, ask for patches. Set a date to stop smoking, try to find someone to 'buddy' with.	Visit 'NHS Stop Smoking' services.

Week	1	2	3
Stress	Spend ten minutes each day positively relaxing.	Spend ten minutes each day positively relaxing.	Spend ten minutes each day positively relaxing.

b)
The potential physical, social and emotional effects on the individual who achieves their targets in the action plan.

When Deidre achieves her targets she should find that she has changed her lifestyle for the better.

Smoking:

By giving up smoking Deidre will gain the following physical benefits:

- Reduce her risk of illness, disability or death caused by cancer, heart disease and lung diseases.
- Reduce her risk of gangrene or amputation caused by circulation problems.
- Protect the health of the people she cares about by not making them breathe her second-hand smoke.
- Reduce the chances of her granddaughter suffering from asthma or glue ear.
- Improve her breathing and general fitness, so not getting out of breath when walking or running for the bus.

Socially Deidre will find that she enjoys the taste of food more. She will also not have to go outside to smoke which many places now insist on.

The emotional effects that Deidre will find include people finding that she is more pleasant to be near! Her clothes and body no longer smell of stale smoke, her house will smell more pleasant.

Diet:

By improving her nutritional intake Deidre will improve her physical health, it can help prevent diseases such as cancer, stroke, heart disease, diabetes and osteoporosis; help maintain optimum body weight; and improve her overall wellbeing.

Although the main benefits of a healthy diet are long-term, Deidre will notice some immediate effects from digesting more nutritious foods. Whilst healthy eating may not produce the instant gratification that exercise does, by changing her diet for the better Deidre will feel the emotional benefits that give a sense achievement as she takes control of her health and will also, among other benefits, improve her digestive system.

A healthy, well balanced diet is full of delicious food; the social benefits that Deidre will benefit from include eating a much more varied diet and enjoy eating from a much wider range of products, she could enjoy experimenting foods from a range of international restaurants.

Exercise

Deidre will find that the benefits of exercise are enormous; physically exercise will increase the efficiency of her heart and lungs and reduce the risk of heart attack and stroke; it will help improve high blood pressure; reduce the risk of osteoporosis; increase strength and stamina.

Emotionally: being physically active on a regular basis will lift depression because the body's own "feel-good hormones" are stimulated; exercise will help improve anxiety and mental and physical alertness so reducing Deidre's stress levels; exercise helps promote healthy sleep.

Socially exercise can increase Deidre's circle of friends if she chooses to join a keep fit group or dance class.

Stress

Deidre will have been reducing her levels of stress as her changes in life style improve the physical, social and emotional aspects of her life. By dealing with stress better Deidre will cope with the anxiety and worry that her family cause her. Deidre will find that as she no longer lets problems cause her distress her blood pressure will remain lowered and her general health and well being will improve. With these improvements will come clearer thinking and better concentration. Deidre will find that she is sleeping and better – by sleeping better she is able to manage her time better.

Some of the emotional benefits of managing stress include: an increased quality of life and well-being, and reduced anxiety, depression, and irritability

Socially, as Deidre becomes less stressed and anxious she will find that she is able to enjoy her social life much more, and her friends and family will find that she is nicer to be with.

c)
List and describe the factors that might influence the individual to adhere to or to give up their action plan.

Deidre's ability to stick to her action plan will depend not only on her will power but she will be influenced by those she is close to, her friends and family, their encouragement and support – or otherwise, will play a large part in how well Deidre achieves her goals.

Deidre will stand a much better chance of succeeding if she realises the benefits of complying with the plan, in addition the dangers of continuing with her current life-style should be explained fully.

Cost sometimes plays a part in failure to achieve goals – inability to afford gym fees could be considered a draw-back, alternative methods of achieving the same results should be explained. A social reason for failure to achieve could be linked to age – if Deidre does not want to acknowledge that she is getting old she might not want to acknowledge that she is developing age and life style related diseases.

Another contributory factor to Deidre's success is the part that the media play – if there has been a recent advertising campaign encouraging behaviour change she may will want to be part of the changes.

A major contributory factor to Deidre's success would be a 'Buddy' scheme. If Deidre has a good friend or partner who undertakes the same life-style changes she is more likely to succeed as they will encourage each other.

Tutor Feedback

Name: Jenny Smith

Task 3 (P3, M2, D1)

Jenny, you have assessed your chosen individual – Deidre Barlow – and devised a realistic action plan for her. Introducing the changes over a period of time is a good idea. This is a good action plan and should Deidre choose to stick with it she should feel much healthier!

You have achieved P3

You have discussed the physical, social and emotional aspects of each of the targets in some depth tackling a difficult task well.

You have achieved D1.

You have described some factors which may influence the ability of the individual to adhere to an action plan and have met the criteria. You might have also considered difficulties of access to and availability of resources e.g. shops for fresh fruit and vegetables, money for transport to shops and recreational facilities. In addition the local environment might not be suitable for jogging or for going out at night unaccompanied.

You have achieved M2.

A well written assignment that meets all the assessment criteria.

Well done, Jenny!